Lighting
at Work

HSG38

HSE BOOKS

This guidance is issued by the Health and
Safety Executive. Following the guidance is
not compulsory and you are free to take other
action. But if you do follow the guidance you
will normally be doing enough to comply with
the law. Health and safety inspectors seek to
secure compliance with the law and may refer
to this guidance as illustrating good practice.

Contents

Introduction

1   This guidance explains how lighting contributes to the health and safety of people at work. Although it is aimed primarily at those responsible for health and safety at work, employees may also find it useful.

2   The guide deals with:

○ assessing and managing the health and safety risks attributable to lighting in the workplace;

○ lighting in the workplace - good practice;

○ minimum recommended illumination levels for health and safety in the workplace.

3   It does not explain how lighting can be used to maximise task performance, or to enhance the appearance of the workplace. Although these are matters of good practice they are not essential for health and safety. Relevant publications giving further information are listed in *Further reading*.

Why is good lighting at work important?

4   Lighting at work is very important to the health and safety of everyone using the workplace. The quicker and easier it is to see a hazard, the more easily it is avoided. The types of hazard present at work therefore determine the lighting requirements for safe operation.

5   Poor lighting can not only affect the health of people at work causing symptoms like eyestrain, migraine and headaches, but it is also linked to Sick Building Syndrome in new and refurbished buildings. Symptoms of this include headaches, lethargy, irritability and poor concentration.

Costs of poor lighting to business

6   Poor lighting at work can represent a significant cost to business in the form of:

○   time off work as a result of accidents and injuries;

○   increased absenteeism;

○   reduced staff efficiency and productivity.

Who is responsible for lighting at work and what are their legal responsibilities?

7   Employers, the self-employed and people in control of non-domestic premises have a duty to ensure that lighting is safe and does not pose a health risk to employees and others who may use their premises.

8   Employers are also required to consult their employees on health and safety matters. Where safety representatives have been appointed by a recognised trade union, it is part of their function to advise during the consultation process. Where employees are not covered by trade union-appointed safety representatives, employers should consult employees directly or via representatives elected for this purpose.

9   Employees also have a duty not to endanger their own or others' health and safety while at work. Further information on legal responsibilities is outlined in Appendix 2.

Managing the health and safety risks from lighting in the workplace

10   The Management of Health and Safety at Work Regulations 1999 (MHSW) require employers to have arrangements in place to cover health and safety. This includes lighting which needs to be suitable and adequate to meet the requirements of the Workplace (Health, Safety and Welfare) Regulations 1992. The following principles can be used to manage health and safety in the workplace.

Planning

11   Employers need to identify priorities and set targets for improvement. For example, they will need to assess whether the lighting design is suitable and safe for the type of work being done. They also need to consider any future changes in the work conditions as this may require different lighting design. The costs and benefits of different lighting design will then need to be considered together with the suitability of lighting for the workplace.

Organisation

12   Organising for health and safety involves the provision of staff with the necessary training and appropriate equipment to do their job safely. This includes those responsible for lighting maintenance. Employers also need to ensure that staff are aware of their responsibility towards their own health and safety and that of other people. For example, it is important that employees notify their employers, or those responsible for health and safety, if lighting is faulty or damaged.

13   Employers need to include staff in the planning and promotion of health and safety, as it is often staff that are the first to notice any health and safety hazards. If employers involve staff it will ensure that they are committed to improving health and safety at work.

Control

14   Controlling health and safety risks includes the setting of standards and maintaining them. Standards set need to be realistic and measurable, and may include lighting maintenance, which can coincide with general maintenance so that it does not interfere with work activities. This would then ensure that lighting is checked on a regular basis and that correct lighting levels are maintained.

Monitoring

15   The monitoring and reviewing of lighting conditions is important in ensuring proper health and safety performance. Monitoring involves checking how far set standards have been met. Reviewing involves the checking of standards, planning, control and organisation and changing them when necessary to improve health and safety. For example, installing new lighting designs may create different health and safety risks; therefore standards may need to be changed or altered.

Risk assessment

16   Under the Management of Health and Safety at Work Regulations 1999 (MHSW), employers must assess possible risks in the workplace. In practice, this includes considering whether work lighting arrangements are satisfactory, or whether they pose any significant risks to staff using the workplace. Where there is a possible risk to employees, action needs to be taken to remove, reduce or control the risk.

17   A **hazard** is anything that may cause harm. A **risk** is the chance, great or small, that an employee will be harmed by a hazard. *Five steps to risk assessment*[1] helps employers to assess the risks in the workplace. These five steps are:

Step 1: Look for the hazards

18   It is important that employers look closely at lighting in the workplace to see what may cause harm or injury. Examples of lighting hazards are given in paragraph 24.

Step 2: Decide who might be harmed and how

19   Employers must consider their employees and any others who might be affected by work activities, and assess the hazards to which they may be exposed as a result of lighting.

Step 3: Evaluate the risks

20   Employers must consider whether their existing precautions are adequate. If not, they must take action to remove, reduce or control the risk. A common problem is inadequate lighting in the actual work area. Steps taken to solve this may include the cleaning of luminaires and replacing failed lamps. If this does not work, alternative action needs to be taken, such as removing obstructions or providing local lighting. To assess whether the lighting is adequate and safe, employers may also need to consider how quickly and accurately employees have to see their work.

21   If there is no risk present, then no action is necessary. To check if the risks are acceptable, employers can obtain further information about legal standards from *Essentials of health and safety at work*.[2]

Step 4: Record the findings

22   Employers who have five or more employees are required by law to record any significant findings from a risk assessment. It is important to record the findings so that:

○   those in the workplace are aware of the hazards and are better placed to deal with them;

○   employers can use these records to assess risks and take appropriate action;

○   any action taken may be referred to in the future if a similar hazard needs to be addressed.

Step 5: Review the assessment regularly

23   It is important for employers to check the risk assessment from time to time, especially when there is a change in working procedures. The assessment needs to take into account any new lighting hazards, including changes of use which might present new lighting hazards and cause harm to the health and safety of employees or others affected by the change in working conditions.

Assessing lighting in the workplace

It is important that lighting in the workplace:

●   allows people to notice hazards and assess risks;

●   is suitable for the environment and the type of work (for example, it is not located against surfaces or materials that may be flammable);

●   provides sufficient light (illuminance on the task);

●   allows people to see properly and discriminate between colours, to promote safety;

●   does not cause glare, flicker or stroboscopic effects;

- avoids the effects of veiling reflections;

- does not result in excessive differences in illuminance within an area or between adjacent areas;

- is suitable to meet the special needs of individuals;

- does not pose a health and safety risk itself;

- is suitably positioned so that it may be properly maintained or replaced, and disposed of to ensure safety;

- includes, when necessary, suitable and safe emergency lighting.

Lighting hazards

24   There are several lighting hazards in the workplace which can affect the health and safety of people. Typical risks from lighting originate from:

lighting effects;

- incorrect lighting design (see pages 18-27);

- improper lighting installation, maintenance, replacement and disposal (see pages 32-34);

improper selection of emergency lighting (see page 34-36).

Lighting effects

Glare

25   Glare occurs when one part of the visual field is much brighter than the average brightness to which the visual system is adapted. When there is direct interference with vision the condition is known as disability glare. Where vision is not directly impaired but there is discomfort, annoyance, irritability or distraction the condition is called discomfort glare. The latter is related to symptoms of visual fatigue. Both types of glare can arise from the same source.

Figure 1 *Disability glare from a light fitting*

Colour effects

26   A surface lit by different artificial light sources, or by daylight under changing sky conditions, may appear to vary in colour. Where colour discrimination is required (as for some electrical work) this can affect safety, but with most light sources the change in colour appearance is insufficient to create problems.

27   Under monochromatic light sources, such as low pressure sodium discharge lamps, colours will not be identifiable and a hazard may go unnoticed. At very low illuminances, colour vision fails and all colours are seen as shades of grey. The section on lighting recommendations in this guide suggests lighting levels which will prevent this effect.

Stroboscopic effects

28   Lamps that operate from an alternating electrical supply may produce oscillations in light output. When the magnitude of these oscillations is great, machinery will appear to be stationary or moving in a different manner. This is called the stroboscopic effect. It is not common with modern lighting systems, but where it does occur it can be dangerous; so appropriate action should be taken to avoid it.

Flicker

29   Light modulation at lower frequencies (about 50 Hz or less) which is visible to most people, is called flicker. The eye is particularly sensitive to flicker and it is especially detectable at the edges of the visual system's field of view. Flicker can, depending on individual sensitivity, be a source of both discomfort and fatigue. It may even cause epileptic seizures in some people. Therefore it needs to be avoided.

Veiling reflections

30   Veiling reflections are high luminance reflections which overlay the detail of the task. Such reflections may be sharp-edged or vague in outline, but regardless of form they can affect task performance and cause discomfort.

Radiation

31   Optical radiation can be harmful if too much enters the eye or falls on unprotected skin. Most people are well aware of the sunburn and skin cancer risks associated with too much exposure to the sun's damaging ultraviolet rays. It is also important to understand that the visible emissions from the sun would damage our sight if we forced ourselves to stare at it for an extended period.

Figure 2 *The reflection of a window is masking information on the screen*

Figure 3 *Distracting reflection close to the line of sight*

Visible radiation

32   Like the sun, optical radiation emitted by manufactured lighting
equipment is predominantly at visible wavelengths. Consequently it is very
difficult to overexpose people because they will automatically look away
when dazzled by an excessively bright source. The radiation from most
lighting equipment is therefore quite safe and employers will not need to
complete an assessment of radiation output. However, there are a few
exceptions, the most important of which are listed below.

Infrared and ultraviolet radiation

33   Some lamp designs also produce significant emissions at infrared and
ultraviolet wavelengths, both of which are invisible; employees could
therefore be exposed to hazards without knowing it and would also not be
able to avoid exposure. Some of the lamps and applications that need
special consideration are listed below.

Problem sources

34   The lamps and lighting applications listed below are capable of causing
excessive personal exposure in some circumstances and it is therefore
important that employers properly assess the risks and take appropriate safety
measures. Manufacturers and suppliers should also provide adequate health
and safety information to users to enable lamps to be used safely. In
particular, it is important to specify any personal protective equipment needs,
for example eye protection.

(a)   Tungsten halogen lamps used in office desktop and close range
      spotlight applications

      These operate at high temperatures and may emit significant amounts
      of ultraviolet radiation which can be harmful to the skin and cornea of
      the eye when they are used close to people (ie within a metre or so) for
      extended periods. The luminaires in which these lamps are used
      should be fitted with an ultraviolet filter which should be checked
      periodically and replaced if damaged. If the luminaire has no filter, it
      should not be used for close-work applications.

(b)   High intensity discharge lamps, carbon-arc and short-arc lamps

These also emit significant amounts of ultraviolet radiation, usually at levels that exceed those from tungsten halogen lamps. However, like tungsten halogen designs, they should be fitted with a safety shield or ultraviolet filter as part of the lamp's glass envelope. Safety shields should be replaced immediately if damaged.

(c)   High-power lamps used in theatres, broadcasting studios and entertainment

These applications require very high output lighting for filming and performance work. Often the level of illumination required exceeds that of a bright summer's day and the very high-power lamps that are used can be so bright that they are capable of damaging eyesight before people can avert their eyes. These lamps can also emit high levels of infrared and ultraviolet radiation. Manufacturers and suppliers must ensure that their products can be used without exposing people above relevant internationally accepted personal exposure limits (see *Threshold limit values for chemical substances and physical agents* and *IRPA guidelines on protection against non-ionising radiation* in *Further reading*, page 59) and, where user precautions are necessary, that appropriate health and safety information is given to the user. This information should include maintenance requirements, user precautions, user training and personal protective equipment requirements. Users should ensure that the necessary health and safety information is obtained from the supplier and that it is followed.

(d)   Display lasers

Some entertainment applications employ lasers to create lighting effects. HSE guidance *The radiation safety of lasers used for display purposes*[3] gives comprehensive information on the radiation safety of these applications.

Managing lighting hazards

35   There are many simple measures that can be taken to eliminate or reduce health and safety risks from lighting hazards. The following table provides some checks and solutions to typical lighting hazards in the workplace.

Hazards	Checks	Solutions
Insufficient light on the task	• check illuminance levels are in line with lighting recommendations (see page 37) • check spacing mounting height ratio against manufacturer's data • check for veiling reflections	• clean lamps and luminaires • replace failed lamps • increase reflectance of room surfaces, for example change decor to light colours • remove obstructions • decrease spacing of luminaires or provide more fittings • provide local lighting • move the working area
Uneven lighting	• check illuminance levels across the working plane and across surrounding areas • check that the ceilings and walls are adequately lit • check spacing /mounting height ratio against manufacturer's data	• replace failed lamps and clean luminaires • provide additional luminaires • decrease spacing between luminaires • change luminaires to give wider light distribution and more upward light without causing glare • increase the reflectance of room surfaces • remove any obstructions
Luminaires too bright	• evaluate effect of luminaire brightness by shielding eyes with hand	• if bare lamps are used, fit some form of light controller or move outside the exclusion zone (Figure 18)

Hazards	Checks	Solutions
Luminaires too bright	• for bare lamps check whether the lamps are within the exclusion zone (see section on minimum lighting recommendations)	• if linear luminaires are used, change the orientation to provide an end-on view • raise height of luminaire, if the reduction in luminance is acceptable • increase reflectance of room surfaces against which luminaires are seen
Natural light seen through windows or roof lights too bright	• check the effects of sky brightness by shielding direct view of window and/or roof light	• fit blinds to windows and whitewash roof lights • ensure that the walls and ceiling areas surrounding the windows and roof lights have a high reflectance • rearrange work to avoid looking towards windows/ roof lights
Excessive range of brightness	• check reflectances of surfaces, particularly those around the task area • check location and relative outputs of luminaires	• increase/decrease the reflectances of the room surfaces which are too low/too high • use diffusing panels • reposition lights • add or change lights to provide more even illuminance
Bright reflected images adjacent to the task	• check whether there are any reflected images in the normal viewing position • locate sources of bright image by placing mirror on the image and looking at it from the worker's position	• change workstation surface from a shiny to a matt finish • reposition task area • reposition sources of brightness • avoid fluorescent lighting • use a high 'thermal inertia' lamp such as an incandescent filament design

Hazards	Checks	Solutions
Reduced contrast of task because of veiling reflections	• evaluate degree of veiling reflections (see Figure 2, page 10) • locate sources of veiling reflections by placing mirror on the task and looking at it from the worker's position (see Figure 4, page 16)	• change workstation surface to a matt finish • move the workstation • move any bright sources • provide local lighting • increase levels of illuminance between areas by increasing reflectance of room surfaces
Strong shadows on the task	• place a thin object, eg a pen, on the work surface and note the number and strength of any shadows	• increase the reflectance of the room surfaces • change the luminaires or their spacings to provide a more even illuminance • increase number of luminaires • provide local or task lighting
Flicker	• no test required	• change lamps near the end of their life • check electrical circuit for any faults in the supply • use high frequency control gear • supply adjacent rows of luminaires from different phases of the electricity supply
Stroboscopic effects	• no test required	• supply adjacent rows of luminaires from different phases of the electricity supply • provide a high frequency supply • replace or take away local lighting • use high frequency control gear where applicable

Hazards	Checks	Solutions
Tasks are difficult to see	• identify which aspects of the task need to be seen and their background • check illuminance is suitable • check the task is free from veiling reflections and shadows	• ensure task background is clear • provide appropriate lighting to see details clearly • increase contrast between the task and the background • provide magnification

Figure 4 *Checking for the presence of veiling reflections*

Figure 5 *Strong shadows cast on work*

Figure 6 *Uneven luminance caused by obstruction from stored goods*

Lighting in the workplace: Good practice

36   To ensure lighting is suitable and sufficient, several aspects of lighting and the workplace need to be considered. These include:

o   lighting design;

o   type of work;

o   the work environment;

o   health aspects;

o   individual requirements;

o   lighting maintenance, replacement and disposal;

o   emergency lighting.

Lighting design and considerations

37   All lighting installations, interior and exterior, are comprised of a lamp(s), a luminaire, and a control system.

Interior and exterior installations

38   The amount of light on a surface affects our ability to see. The finer the detail, the higher the illuminance required.

39   Both interior and exterior lighting need to achieve a reasonable uniform illuminance in all relevant working areas, ie illuminance across any given task area needs to be uniform. For more information see CIBSE *Code for lighting.*[4]

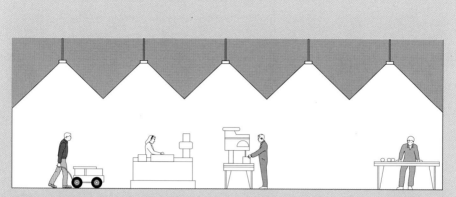

Figure 7a *General lighting*

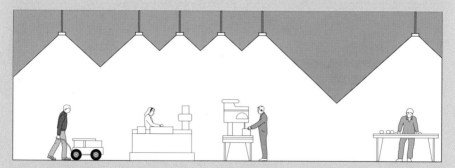

Figure 7b *Localised lighting*

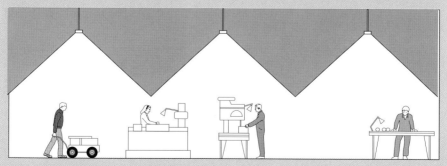

Figure 7c *Local lighting*

40   Lighting design should take account of the effect of shadows cast, whether these are objects and/or people in the work environment. Light sources should be positioned to minimise these effects. For example, it is not good practice to illuminate machinery or a protrusion from below, as the shadows may lead to confusion and an accident.

41   The type of lighting installation chosen depends on:

- its suitability for use;

- whether it is safe for use;

- the size of area to be covered;

- the physical constraints of the space;

- the purpose for which it will be used.

Interior lighting

42   Interior lighting can be split into three categories:

- general;

- localised;

- local.

General lighting provides uniform illumination over the whole working area and does not limit positioning of the work (Figure 7a).

Localised lighting provides different levels of illumination in different parts of the same working area. It matches the level of illumination to the needs of specific tasks (Figure 7b).

Local lighting is usually a combination of background lighting and a luminaire close to the actual work area. It is used when:

(a)   a high level of illumination is needed in a small area;

(b)   flexible directional lighting is required, for example when doing different tasks at a workstation;

Figure 8 *General indoor lighting*

Figure 9 *Local lighting providing flexible, directional lighting*

Figure 10 *Example of general and local lighting in a factory*

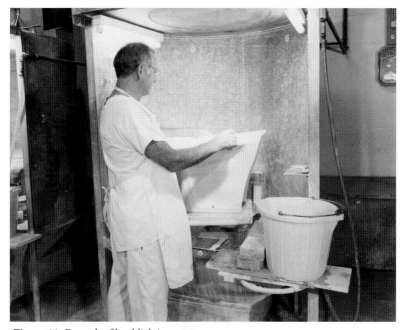

Figure 11 *Example of local lighting*

Figure 12 *Local lighting of a small area to a high illuminance*

(c)   general lighting is unnecessary or impossible to install because of the layout of the work area (Figure 7c).

43   Choosing lighting is a matter of judgement. There is no single best approach. However, the lamp and the luminaire need to be selected as a package, because each luminaire is designed for a limited range of lamps.

44   If a group of luminaires is selected, the spacing between them needs to be considered. Manufacturers publish maximum spacing/mounting height ratios for each luminaire. If these are exceeded there will be excessive variation in illuminance across the working plane.

45   Where illuminance on vertical surfaces is important, it may be necessary to space the luminaires closer together than the maximum spacing/mount ratio given by the supplier, to ensure that the illuminance is evenly distributed across all vertical surfaces. However, placing luminaires closer together need not apply where there is a regularly arranged obstruction, for example in works stores. In this case the spacing between fittings needs to match the spacing of the obstruction (Figure 14) For more information see CIBSE Lighting guide LG01.[5]

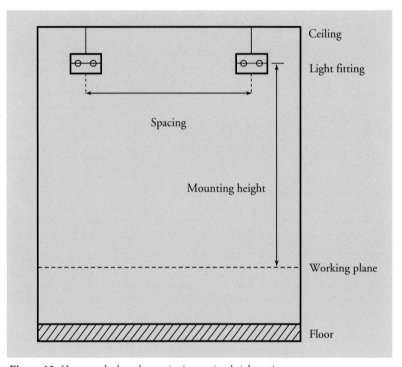

Figure 13 *How to calculate the spacing/mounting height ratio*

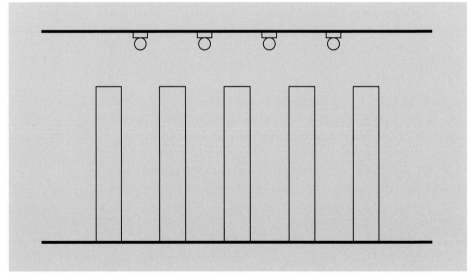

Figure 14 *Obstruction to a regular array of light fittings. The spacing of the light fittings should be matched to the spacing of the obstruction*

46   Where linear luminaires with tubular fluorescent lamps are used, the position and angle of the luminaire must be considered, as well as spacing. Such luminaires are less glaring if viewed end-on, rather than sideways-on. A regular arrangement of luminaires should therefore be positioned so that they are end-on to the viewing direction with the longest dimension. Corridors are an extreme example; it is generally better to align linear luminaires along the corridor rather than across it.

47   The position of local luminaires is important as it determines both the illuminance on the workstation as well as the degree of glare. Further guidance on interior lighting design can be found in CIBSE Lighting guides LG01[5] and LG07.[6]

Exterior lighting

In general all exterior installations should:

  achieve a reasonably uniform illuminance on all relevant work areas;

  avoid glare to the users of those areas and to occupants of nearby areas.

48   The Department for Environment, Food and Rural Affairs and CIBSE can give further advice on how to avoid excessive light affecting others, particularly in the countryside.

49   Illuminances provided need to be consistent with the lighting recommendations suggested in this guidance. To avoid excessive contrast in illuminance, luminaires should not be spaced too far apart. This is important in security lighting where a variation in light levels may pose a safety risk. Glare is determined by the light distribution of fittings, their mounting height and, for floodlights, the direction of aiming.

50   With large areas, the lighting design chosen depends upon:

  the degree of obstruction;

  whether illuminance is required primarily on horizontal or vertical planes.

Figure 15 *Floodlighting, by predominantly downward lighting, of an area where obstruction can occur*

51   Where obstruction is likely and where illuminance on the horizontal plane is important, for example in lorry parks, lighting should be overhead from a height that minimises shadows.

52   If obstruction is slight and vertical illuminance is required, floodlighting projectors can be used. However, care needs to be taken to avoid glare.

53   When choosing the mounting height of luminaires, the following should be considered:

○   cost;

○   planning laws;

○   positions where poles/towers can be placed;

○   level of glare that is acceptable;

○   ease of maintenance required.

54   For internal private roads, the road surfaces and surroundings need to be lit to enable vehicles and objects to appear in silhouette. Advice on suitable layouts is given in BS 5489 *Road lighting*.[7] Lighting that gives good colour definition also enables pedestrians to identify other people and/or vehicles clearly.

55   Where the periphery of a building is to be lit, wall-mounted fittings may be used. These can be simple projector floodlights or bulkhead fittings, provided they are suitable for external use.

56   Wall-mounted, pole-mounted, or bollard-type fittings can be used for entrance areas. Again, spacing and light distribution determines the uniformity of illuminance. Fittings need to be carefully chosen to minimise glare for people entering or leaving the building.

57   Outside workplaces (especially construction sites) tend to have temporary lighting installations and portable lighting , including hand lamps. The lighting objectives for temporary installations should be the same as for permanent ones, although the extra wear and tear on temporary equipment will have safety implications for the choice of equipment, the means of fixing and the source of electricity. Extensive guidance on the lighting of construction sites is given in *Electrical safety on construction sites*.[8]

Lamps and luminaires

58   A wide range of lamps is commercially available. Different lamp types produce light in different ways and so have different properties. Characteristics of lamps widely used for lighting at work are summarised in the tables in Appendix 1. More detailed information is given in the Lighting Industry Federation's *Lamp guide*.[9]

59   The choice of lamp depends on certain factors, such as the type of workplace in which it is to be used, luminous efficiency and service life (Appendix 1). Lamps and luminaires must:

o   support and protect the light source;

o   provide safe electrical connection;

o   be safe for installation, use and maintenance;

o   where practicable, provide filtering to remove harmful levels of radiation.

60   Guidance on luminaire types, their standards and markings is available in CIBSE *Code for lighting*.[4] Each luminaire is designed for a specific lamp or range of lamps. If lamps are put in the wrong luminaires this may result in glare and decrease the life and operating efficiency of the lamp. Using luminaires in situations for which they are not designed (for example, low-pressure sodium lamps in a potentially wet environment) can be dangerous. Expert advice is available in CIBSE *Lighting in hostile and hazardous environments* LG/HHE.[10]

Lighting control systems

61   A control system can be anything from a simple mechanical switch to a sophisticated automatic control system capable of responding to the amount of daylight present, or to area occupancy.

62   Do not place manually operated switches in a position where employees have to reach past machinery or cross an unlit area to operate them. Similar considerations apply to automatic control systems. Lighting installations with such systems should include a 'fail safe' facility so that if the control system fails, no occupied area will be plunged into darkness.

Automatic control systems also need to include a manual override which can be used if the automatic system fails.

Type of work

63   Employers need to consider the type of work that is to be carried out when deciding on a suitable lighting design. For example, if a task requires detailed work, local lighting may be needed in addition to general lighting so that the work can be carried out safely.

64   Specialised work, for example electronic assembly, may require workers to differentiate between the colours of wire. In these circumstances employers will need to consider lighting that does not affect the natural appearance of colours so that their employees can work safely.

The work environment

65   Aspects of the work environment that need to be considered are:

○   level of natural light;

○   interior design;

○   working conditions.

Level of natural light

66   Most people prefer to work in natural daylight, therefore it is important to make full use of it. Daylight by itself does not usually provide sufficient illuminance throughout the whole working area or for the entire working day; in most circumstances sufficient and suitable lighting can be provided by a combination of natural and artificial lighting. However, some workplaces have no natural light owing to architectural layout, and in these cases suitable artificial lighting needs to be present, so that work can be done safely and efficiently.

Figure 16 *Natural lighting is blocked out and replaced by artificial lighting to avoid glare*

67   Natural light on its own, or combined with artificial lighting, can be a source of glare and/or reflections. Where it is not possible to adjust the position or location of the display screen or work station, adjusting the illuminance in the workplace may solve the problem. If not, anti-glare screens for VDUs may be used as a last resort.

Interior design

68   Constraints imposed by the layout of the workplace may result in the employer choosing a particular lighting design. For example, an open-plan office with large windows will have different lighting requirements to small individual offices with few windows.

69   Furniture and equipment in an open-plan office may cause excessive differences in the illuminance between areas; lighting design needs to allow

for this, especially in areas where illuminance may be insufficient to carry out a task safely.

70 The choice of colour in a room is also important because dark surfaces reflect very little light. Light reflected off the walls is usually distributed more evenly than direct lighting. It can soften shadows and will tend to reduce the effects of any veiling reflections and glare. The reflectance of surfaces may be calculated by using a method outlined in BS 4800: *Specification for paint colours for building purposes.*[11]

Working conditions

71 It is important that an employer considers the working conditions in which lighting is used. Conditions which create dusty, flammable or explosive atmospheres may require a lighting design that protects against dust ingress, is robustly constructed and does not ignite. Care must also be taken to keep away any objects (for example curtains and shelves) that may be damaged by lamps that operate at high temperatures (for example tungsten halogen). Guidance on lighting in hazardous areas can be sought from CIBSE *Lighting in hostile and hazardous environments* LG/HHE.[10]

Health aspects

72 Poor lighting makes the visual system work harder and may lead to symptoms commonly described as eyestrain. Symptoms of eyestrain vary according to the lighting conditions and the task being carried out. They can disappear after taking adequate rest or breaks away from a particular activity. Symptoms include:

○ irritation, eg inflammation of the eyes and lids;

○ itchiness;

○ breakdown of vision, blurred or double vision;

○ referred symptoms, eg headaches, fatigue, giddiness.

73 Poor lighting can also cause other, more indirect effects. The natural response to insufficient illuminance or veiling reflections, for example, is to get closer to the task or to look at it from a different direction. This can

mean adopting unsuitable postures that lead to other forms of discomfort such as neck- and backache.

Individual requirements

74   It is important that employers take into account the needs of individuals when assessing their lighting requirements. This should improve employee comfort and well-being. For example, some people may prefer to work with little artificial lighting or low levels of luminance; various lamps have adjustable fittings and controls that can accommodate these needs.

75   The Workplace (Health, Safety and Welfare) Regulations 1992 require employers, or those who have control over health and safety in the workplace, to take into account employees with special needs. For example, light flicker may trigger seizures in some people with epilepsy. Employers will need to prevent this risk by providing appropriate lighting or adequate control measures.

Lighting maintenance, replacement and disposal

76   Lamps/luminaires need to be kept clean and replaced, as illuminance levels decline with age. For details on the maintenance of illuminance levels see CIBSE *Code for lighting*.[4] How often they are maintained and replaced depends on the type of lamp/luminaire and the environmental conditions. For example, if the lamp/luminaire is out of reach and therefore infrequently cleaned and is in a dirty, corrosive environment, it will need to be replaced more often than the same equipment in a typical office environment. Also, there needs to be safe and easy access to remote luminaires that require cleaning, repairing or replacing.

77   Ensure that luminaires are intact and undamaged, as this may pose a health and safety risk to employees. Damaged luminaires may expose dangerous live electrical parts. They may also present a health hazard. Information on the use of high-wattage tungsten halogen lamps can be sought from the luminaire manufacturer or the Lighting Industry Federation.

Figure 17 *Floodlighting by projectors of an area free from obstructions*

78   When replacing lamps in existing luminaires, care needs to be taken to ensure that the lamp and control gear are electrically and physically compatible. For example, a 110-volt lamp should not be fitted in a 240-volt light fitting. In addition, the overall dimensions of the lamp should be suitable for the luminaire. If they are incompatible the lamp may become damaged; or, alternatively, the lamp, luminaire, or control gear may overheat causing a fire risk.

79   When carrying out maintenance, it is important to ensure that safety procedures are properly followed and do not interfere with other work activities. Planned and regular maintenance is good practice. This ensures that lighting is safe and illuminance levels are maintained.

80   Regular maintenance should include:

○   cleaning lamp/luminaires;

○   repairing and replacing damaged or ineffective lamps/luminaires;

○   maintaining emergency lighting (proper cleaning, repairing, replacing and disposal);

○   disposing of lamps/luminaires safely.

81   Emergency lighting needs to be tested and checked at regular intervals to ensure that it works properly in the event of normal lighting failure. The more hazardous the environment, the more frequently it needs to be checked. It is also important to have back-up measures in place to detect or prevent emergency lighting failure.

82   Lamps need to be disposed of carefully. Some manufacturers operate take-back schemes, and some refuse-disposal agencies will take broken lamps. Broken glass is an obvious safety hazard, so eye protection and gloves should be provided to reduce the risk of injury. Purpose-built lamp crushing machines can be used for breaking lamps to reduce their bulk. Some lamp crushing machines contain water, and the sodium in low-pressure sodium lamps can ignite when in contact with water, so care should be taken when using lamp crushing machines. If there is any doubt about the suitability of a machine you should always consult the manufacturer for further advice.

83   Some lamps pose hazards to health, including those containing dusts such as phosphor, or vapours such as mercury. Disposal of these lamps should be in a well-ventilated area or outdoors. The outer envelope of high-pressure sodium lamps can be broken but the inner tubes are strong and contain mercury. It is strongly recommended that the inner tube is left intact.

84   Employers need to ensure that employees are protected from dangerous substances to which they may be exposed in the maintenance and disposal of lamps. It is also the employer's duty under the Control of Substances Hazardous to Health Regulations 2002 (COSHH), to prevent, or where this is not reasonably practicable, to adequately control exposure of employees to substances hazardous to health.

Emergency lighting

85   Employers need to consider several factors when choosing emergency lighting that is sufficient and suitable:

○ The lighting needs to be activated for as long as the danger exists, or until normal lighting is resumed for work activities to continue safely;

○ When normal lighting fails, immediate light output is necessary. This can be acquired only from certain lamp types such as tungsten, tungsten halogen and tubular fluorescent lamps. Other lamp types take too long to reach full output;

○ A mechanism is required for connecting the lamp to an alternative electrical supply when the normal supply fails;

○ Necessary illuminance needs to be provided at appropriate places, such as emergency exits and escape routes;

○ Direction and fire exit signs need to be illuminated;

○ To prevent glare, emergency luminaires need to be mounted at least two metres above the floor but not much higher, as in the event of a fire there is always a risk of smoke reducing the light levels on the escape route;

○ It is important that the lighting outside the building is adequate for safe evacuation and that the lighting itself is safe for outside use;

86   In deciding the position and location of luminaires, those responsible for health and safety need to consider where:

○ emergency exits are situated;

○ escape routes are located;

○ areas that require special attention are situated, such as escalators, plant rooms, direction signs, fire alarm points and fire-fighting equipment.

87   A wide choice of lighting equipment is available, ranging from luminaires with their own battery packs to centralised systems where the lamps are supplied from a central generator or batteries via protected wiring. The choice of system will depend on the size and nature of the installation. More detailed guidance on the requirements of emergency lighting is given in CIBSE Technical Memorandum 12.[12]

Emergency lighting levels

88   There are two types of emergency lighting:

standby - which enables people to continue working safely;

escape - which enables people to leave a building safely.

Illuminance needed for standby lighting depends on the work activity. It may be between 5% and 100% of the illuminance produced by the normal lighting. The average and minimum measured light levels for different types of work are provided in the section on lighting recommendations.

89   The illuminances required for escape lighting are given in BS 5266 Part 1: *Emergency lighting: Code of practice for emergency lighting of premises other than cinemas and certain other specified premises used for entertainment.*[13] This code of practice recommends that escape lighting should reach the required illuminance for employees to leave the building safely, within five seconds of failure of the main lighting system. If employees are familiar with their workplace this time limit can be extended to fifteen seconds.

90   Battery-powered escape lighting is usually designed to operate for one to three hours. This duration varies according to the size of the building and the likely problems of evacuation. Escape lighting can also be powered by a generator. In general it is important to ensure that battery capacity and/or generator power is adequate for escape lighting so that employees have enough time to leave a building safely.

91   Illuminances for escape routes need to fall within the lighting recommendations for corridors and circulation routes proposed in this guidance. Particular attention needs to be paid to stairs, obstructions and changes in direction when deciding appropriate illuminance levels.

Minimum lighting recommendations

92   These recommendations should provide the minimum light levels necessary for the health and safety of employees. They apply to interior and exterior lighting intended for everyday use, and cover:

o   illuminance on the task;

o   illuminance ratios.

Illuminance on the task

93   The illuminance needed depends on how much detail needs to be seen. It also depends on the age of the worker, and the speed and accuracy by which the task needs to be performed. These perfomance-related requirements and light levels are detailed in the CIBSE *Code for lighting*.[4] The table on page 38 sets out recommended illuminances for different types of work. It makes recommendations for average illuminance for the work area as a whole and for minimum measured illuminance at any position within it. Using only the average illuminance may result in lower illuminances in certain areas. This may endanger the safety of workers. The minimum measured illuminance is the lowest illuminance recommended in the work area for health and safety.

94   Glare on the task: Glare is most commonly experienced when lamps are directly visible close to the line of sight. The greater the light output of the lamp or very bright parts of the luminaire, and the smaller the area from which the light is emitted, the larger will be the angular zone above which a direct view of the lamp should be avoided (see Figure 18 on page 40). This may be done either by keeping bare lamps out of the zone, or by shielding them. The table on page 39 gives the recommended angles for such exclusion zones, based on a simple glare criterion. A more sophisticated system for estimating the degree of glare in a lighting installation is described in the CIBSE *Code for lighting*.[4]

Activity	Typical locations/ types of work	Average illuminance (lux) lx	Minimum measured illuminance (lux) lx
Movement of people, machines and vehicles[a]	Lorry park, corridors, circulation routes	20	5
Movement of people, machines and vehicles in hazardous areas; rough work not requiring any perception of detail	Construction site clearance, excavation and soil work, loading bays, bottling and canning plants	50	20
Work requiring limited perception of detail[b]	Kitchens, factories assembling large components, potteries	100	50
Work requiring perception of detail[c]	Offices, sheet metal work, bookbinding	200	100
Work requiring perception of fine detail[d]	Drawing offices, factories assembling electronic components, textile production	500	200

[a] Only safety has been considered, because no perception of detail is needed and visual fatigue is unlikely. However, where it is necessary to see detail to recognise a hazard or where error in performing the task could put someone else at risk, for safety purposes as well as to avoid visual fatigue, the figure needs to be increased to that for work requiring the perception of detail. The CIBSE *Code for lighting*[4] gives more information and recommendations based on scientific knowledge, practical experience, technical feasibility and economic reality.

[b] The purpose is to avoid visual fatigue; the illuminances will be adequate for safety purposes

[c] The purpose is to avoid visual fatigue; the illuminances will be adequate for safety purposes

[d] The purpose is to avoid visual fatigue; the illuminances will be adequate for safety purposes

95   The exclusion zone criterion can be applied to individual luminaires (including local luminaires) and to regular or irregular arrays. Glare may also arise from lamps which are installed on walls or equipment if the exclusion principles outlined are not followed. It cannot be applied to glare from large sources, for example where the whole ceiling is used as a source of indirect lighting, because the whole of its surface may be too bright. To avoid glare in such circumstances the average illuminance on the ceiling of normal reflectance should not exceed 2250 lx.

96   Severe glare may also be caused by direct sunlight coming in either through windows or rooflights. Window glare can be prevented or reduced by using blinds or tinted glass, and rooflight glare can be effectively reduced by using a white or colour wash. The disadvantage of these measures is that they reduce the amount of daylight in the interior.

Table for exclusion zone angles

Lamp type	Angle for exclusion zone	Comments
Tubular fluorescent lamps	10 degrees	This is for viewing the lamps from the side; viewing the lamps end-on does not require any control
Discharge lamps with a fluorescent coating; incandescent lamps with a frosted glass	20 degrees	
Discharge and incandescent lamps which allow a direct view of the arc tube or the filament	30 degrees	

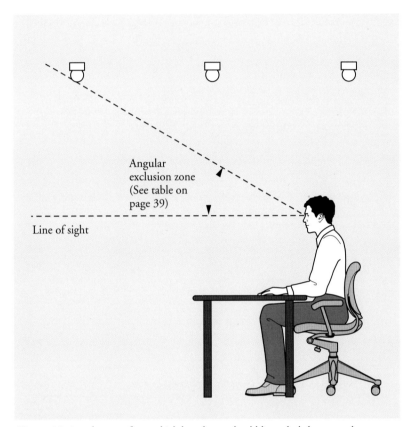

Figure 18 *Angular zone from which bare lamps should be excluded to control discomfort and disability*

Illuminance ratios

97   The relationship between the lighting of the work area and adjacent areas is important. Large differences in illuminance between them may cause visual discomfort or even affect safety in places where there is frequent movement. This problem arises most often where local or localised lighting indoors exposes an employee to a range of illuminances for a long time, or where the movement between interior and exterior working areas exposes an employee to a sudden change of illuminance. To guard against danger and discomfort, the recommendations in the table opposite need to be followed:

Maximum ratios of illuminance for adjacent areas

Situations to which recommendation applies	**Typical location**	**Maximum ratio of illuminance** Working area Adjacent area		
Where each task is individually lit and the area around the task is lit to a lower illuminance	Local lighting in an office	5	:	1
Where two working areas are adjacent , but one is lit to a lower illuminance than the other	Localised lighting in a works store	5	:	1
Where two working areas are lit to different illuminances and are separated by a barrier but there is frequent movement between them	A storage area inside a factory and a loading bay outside	10	:	1

Figure 19 *Transition zone between high- and low-luminance areas*

Figure 20 *Differences in illuminance between interior and exterior area*

98   Where there is a conflict between the recommended average illuminances and the maximum illuminance ratios, it is important to take the higher values.

An example

An interior area is lit to 500 lux. It has an adjacent, but separate area, and there is frequent movement of people between the two. From the recommended maximum illuminance ratios suggested on page 41, the illuminance for the adjacent area would be 50 lux (10:1 ratio). If the only activity carried out in the adjacent area is movement, the suggested average illuminance is 20 lux. However, this would give an illuminance ratio of 25:1 between adjacent areas (ie 500 lux: 20 lux) which is too great as the recommended illuminance ratio is 10:1. In this situation the maximum illuminance ratio of 500 lux: 50 lux should be applied, the adjacent area being lit to 50 lux, at least in the area closest to the doorway. Areas further away can be lit to the recommended average illuminance of 20 lux. In other words a transition zone needs to be provided between the two adjacent areas (see Figure 19).

Appendix 1 Summary of lamp characteristics

1   The tables on pages 45-51 summarises the characteristics of lamp types widely used for light at work. Further detailed information should be available from lamp manufacturers. Explanations of the column headings are as follows (the first and last are self-explanatory):

(a)   Lamp prefix letters: these may be found marked on the lamp or on its packaging and in the UK they are widely used as a means of identification. Additional letters may be added to the end of the construction of the specific lamp, eg F for a fluorescent coating.

(b)   Construction and appearance: entries in this column describe the method of light production and the physical appearance of the lamp.

(c)   Luminous efficacy: this is a measure of how efficiently the lamp converts electrical power (measured in watts) to light (measured in lumens). The higher the value of the luminous efficacy, the more efficient the lamp. A range of values is given for each lamp type because luminous efficacy varies with power. These values do not include the power consumed by any control gear that may be required.

(d)   Life: a lamp can be considered to have reached the end of its life not only when it fails, but also when it flickers markedly or when its efficiency has fallen to an uneconomic level. A range is given for each lamp type as life will depend on the lamp rating, the switching cycle and other operating conditions.

(e)   Apparent colour: the apparent colour of the light emitted by each lamp type.

(f) Colour rendering: the extent to which a lamp type gives surface colours the same appearance as they have under a reference light source, usually daylight. Excellent colour rendering implies no distortion of surface colours.

(g) Run-up time: tungsten, tungsten halogen and tubular fluorescent lamps produce light immediately when switched on. All the other lamp types require several minutes to approach full light output; this may be important where installations have to be used at unexpected times.

(h) Restrike time: tungsten, tungsten halogen and tubular fluorescent lamps can be switched off and then switched on again immediately. All the other lamp types, unless fitted with special control gear, show a significant delay after switch off before they will re-ignite. This property may have important safety implications as momentary interruption in the electricity supply can extinguish these lamps and it may be some time before they can be re-lit.

Summary of lamp characteristics

Name of lamp type	Lamp prefix letters	Construction and appearance	Luminous efficacy (1m/W)	Life (hours)	Apparent colour	Colour rendering	Run-up time (min)	Restrike time (min)	Typical applications
Tungsten		A tungsten filament heated to incandescence in a glass envelope	8-18	1000-2000	Warm white light	Excellent	Immediate	Immediate	Social/commercial interiors such as hotels and shops, display lighting, emergency lighting, hand lamps
Tungsten halogen		A tungsten filament heated to incandescence in a small envelope containing halogens	18-24	2000-4000	Warm white light	Excellent	Immediate	Immediate	Display lighting, area floodlighting
High pressure mercury tungsten blended	MBTF	An electric discharge in a high pressure mercury atmosphere contained in an arc tube in series with a tungsten filament heated to incandescence; the whole contained within a glass envelope with a fluorescent coating	10-26	5000-8000	White light	Moderate	4	10	As a replacement for tungsten lamps when longer lamp life is essential

Summary of lamp characteristics (continued)

Name of lamp type	Lamp prefix letters	Construction and appearance	Luminous efficacy (1m/W)	Life (hours)	Apparent colour	Colour rendering	Run-up time (min)	Restrike time (min)	Typical applications
High pressure mercury*	MBF	An electric discharge in a high-pressure mercury atmosphere contained in an arc tube within a glass envelope with a fluorescent coating. Needs control gear	35-54	5000-10 000	White light	Moderate	4	10	Industrial lighting, road lighting
Metal halide*	MBI	An electric discharge in a high-pressure mercury atmosphere with metal halide additives in an arc tube, sometimes contained within a glass envelope. Needs control gear	66-84	5000-10 000	Depends on the halogens used in the arc tube but tends to cold white light	Good	5	10	Industrial and commercial lighting, area floodlighting

Summary of lamp characteristics (continued)

Name of lamp type	Lamp prefix letters	Construction and appearance	Luminous efficacy (1m/W)	Life (hours)	Apparent colour	Colour rendering	Run-up time (min)	Restrike time (min)	Typical applications
Tubular fluorescent	MCF	An electric discharge in a low-pressure mercury atmosphere contained in a glass tube internally coated with a fluorescent material. Needs control gear	37-90	5000-10 000	Anything from warm white to cold white light	Anything from moderate to excellent depending on the properties of the fluorescent coating	Immediate	Immediate	Industrial and commercial lighting. Rapid development includes compact versions suitable as replacements for tungsten lamps
High-pressure sodium	SON	An electric discharge in a high-pressure sodium atmosphere in an arc tube contained in an outer envelope. Needs control gear	67-121	6000-12 000	Anything from slightly orange to nearly white light	Varies from poor to good depending on the pressure used	5	1	Industrial lighting; area floodlighting; road lighting. Rapid development includes one form with good colour-rendering properties
Low-pressure sodium	SOX/SLI	An electric discharge in a low-pressure sodium atmosphere in a glass arc tube contained in a glass envelope. Needs control gear	101-175	6000-12 000	Yellow light	Non-existent	10	3	Road lighting and security lighting

*This lamp type should not be used if the outer envelope is broken because considerable quantities of ultra-violet radiation will then be emitted.

Summary of light fitting characteristics

Light fitting type	Appearance	Suitable lamp types	Mounting positions	Typical light distribution	Glare control method	Typical application
Globe		Tungsten, compact MCF, MBTF	Pendant	In all directions, with emphasis given by any open part	Glare controlled by reducing brightness of lamp	Offices, social/commerical areas
Cone		Tungsten. compact MCF, MBTF	Pendant	Widespread but downward	Glare controlled by shielding	Offices, industrial premises
Bare batten		MCF	Surface or pendant	In all directions	No control or glare	Offices, industrial premises
Trough reflector		MCF	Surface or pendant	Widespread but downward, some upward light if trough has slots	Glare controlled by shielding	Offices, industrial premises
Linear diffuser		MCF	Surface or pendant	Widespread	Glare controlled by reducing brightness of source	Offices, industrial premises where lamps have to be enclosed
Linear prismatic		MCF	Surface or pendant	Varies widely depending on the characteristics of the prismatic panels	Glare controlled by limiting light distribution	Offices, industrial premises where lamps have to be enclosed
Linear reflector		MCF	Surface or pendant	Directional, exact direction depending on the properties of the reflector	Glare controlled by limiting distribution and by shielding	Offices

Summary of light fitting characteristics (continued)

Light fitting type	Appearance	Suitable lamp types	Mounting positions	Typical light distribution	Glare control method	Typical application
Linear louvre		MCF	Surface or recessed	Widespread but downward	Glare controlled by shielding	Offices
Recessed diffuser		MCF, MBF, MBI, SON	Recessed	Widespread but downward	Glare controlled by reducing brightness of light source	Offices
Recessed prismatic		MCF, MBF, MBI, SON	Recessed	Very variable, depending on characteristics of prismatic panel	Glare controlled by limiting light distribution	Offices
Recessed reflector		MCF, MBF, MBI, SON	Recessed	Directional, depending on the properties of the reflector	Glare controlled by limiting light distribution and by shielding	Offices
Recessed louvre		MCF, MBF, MBI, SON	Recessed	Widespread but downward	Glare controlled by shielding	Offices
Bare lamp reflector		MBFR, SONR	Surface or pendant	Widespread but downward	Glare controlled by thickness of reflecting layer on lamp	High bay industrial premises
Bare lamp reflector with anti-glare skirt		MBFR, SONR	Surface or pendant	Widespread but downward	Glare controlled by shielding	High bay industrial premises

Summary of light fitting characteristics (continued)

Light fitting type	Appearance	Suitable lamp types	Mounting positions	Typical light distribution	Glare control method	Typical application
High bay reflector		MBF, MBI, SON	Surface or pendant	Concentrated downwards	Glare controlled by shielding	High bay industrial premises
Low bay		MBF, MBI, SON	Surface, pendant or recessed	Widespread but downward, depending on whether reflectors, prismatics, diffusers or louvres are used in the fitting	Glare controlled by shielding (unless a diffusing or prismatic cover is used)	Industrial premises where low mounting heights are unavoidable
Coffered ceiling		MCF, MBF, MBI, SON		Widespread	Glare controlled by shielding	Offices
Luminous ceiling		MCF		Widespread	Glare controlled by using translucent material to reduce brightness of lamps and to shield lamps from view	Social/commercial interiors
Uplighters		MBF, MBI, SON	Free-standing, or furniture mounted, or pendant	Widespread but upwards	Glare controlled by shielding	Offices
Downlighters		Tungsten, MBF, Compact MCF	Recessed or surface	Concentrated downwards	Glare controlled by shielding	Office and display areas

Summary of light fitting characteristics (continued)

Light fitting type	Appearance	Suitable lamp types	Mounting positions	Typical light distribution	Glare control method	Typical application
Bulkheads		Tungsten, MBF, SON, SOX, MCF	Surface	Widespread	Little glare control but brightness usually low	Industrial premises, exterior areas
Floodlighting projector		Tungsten halogen, SON, SOX, MBF, MBI		Varies with the shape of the reflector used	No control of glare within beam, shape of beam controlled by reflector used	Industrial area floodlighting, car parks
Street lighting lanterns		SOX, SON, MBF, MBI		Widespread but closely controlled within specified angles	Moderate glare control by limiting light distribution	Road lighting
Hand lamps		Tungsten, MCF		Widespread	Glare controlled by shielding	Industrial premises where severe obstruction occurs

Appendix 2 Legislation

Legislation relating to lighting at work includes:

- Health and Safety at Work etc. Act 1974

- Management of Health and Safety at Work Regulations 1999

- The Workplace (Health, Safety and Welfare) Regulations 1992

- Health and Safety (Display Screen Equipment) Regulations 1992

- Provision and Use of Work Equipment Regulations 1998

- Electricity at Work Regulations 1989

- Control of Substances Hazardous to Health Regulations 1999 (COSHH)

- Health and Safety (Consultation with Employees) Regulations 2002

Other legislation also provides industry with specific guidance on lighting requirements.

The **Health and Safety at Work etc. Act 1974 (HSWA)** places a duty on employers to ensure the health and safety of employees and others who may be affected by their work activities.

In practice this means that lighting should not endanger the health and safety of people at work. The HSWA also places a general duty on lighting manufacturers and suppliers, to make sure that their lighting is safe and does not present a risk to health and safety. This responsibility includes providing instructions on using and maintaining lighting.

The **Management of Health and Safety at Work Regulations 1999** place a duty on employers and self-employed people to assess risks to health and safety from their undertaking. This will include risks from lighting. The duty holder must also identify what measures are needed to comply with health and safety requirements and make arrangements to manage these measures effectively.

The **Workplace (Health, Safety and Welfare) Regulations 1992: Regulation 8** requires every workplace to have suitable and sufficient lighting. The lighting in the workplace, should as far as is possible, be natural. Regulation 8 also states that suitable and sufficient emergency lighting needs to be provided, where people are particularly exposed to danger, in the event of failure of artificial lighting.

The **Health and Safety (Display Screen Equipment) Regulations 1992** seek to reduce the health and safety risks to employees from using visual display units (VDUs) in the workplace. *VDUs: An easy guide to the regulations*[14] summarises the possible risks to health that are associated with display screen equipment work, including poor lighting. Problems may arise if workstations are too brightly or dimly lit, or if light sources are badly positioned, causing screen reflections or glare. The assessment checklist annexed to the VDU guidance[14] also gives advice on achieving comfortable levels of lighting.

The **Provision and Use of Work Equipment Regulations 1998 (PUWER)** lay down health and safety requirements for the provision and use of work equipment. Regulation 21 states that any place where a person uses work equipment should be suitably and sufficiently lit.

PUWER also requires employers to ensure that work equipment, such as lighting, complies with relevant UK legislation implementing EC Directives, for example the Electrical Equipment (Safety) Regulations 1994 which implement the Low Voltage Directive.

The **Electricity at Work Regulations 1989** cover health and safety duties for the safe use of electricity at work. They require electrical systems, such as lighting, to be properly constructed, maintained and fit for the purpose and environment in which they are to be used. They also require that adequate lighting be provided at all electrical equipment on which, or near which, work is being done in circumstances which may give rise to danger.

The **Control of Substances Hazardous to Health Regulations 2002 (COSHH)** provide a framework to help duty holders, who are mainly employers and the self-employed (apart from certain provisions), to protect people in the workplace against health risks from hazardous substances. This includes risks from hazardous substances to which they may be exposed during the maintenance and disposal of lamps. Under COSHH it is also the duty of employers to ensure that employees are properly trained in the risks to health created by exposure in the circumstances of work and the precautions which should be taken.

The **Health and Safety (Consultation with Employees) Regulations 1996** require employers to consult their employees on matters that affect their health and safety. These Regulations apply to employers who have employees that are not covered by representatives appointed by recognised trade unions.

References

1   *Five steps to risk assessment* Leaflet INDG163(rev2) HSE Books 2006
    (single copy free or priced packs of 10 ISBN 978 0 7176 6189 3)
    www.hse.gov.uk/pubns/indg163.pdf

2   *Essentials of health and safety at work* Guidance (Fourth edition) HSE
    Books 2006 ISBN 978 0 7176 6179 4

3   *The radiation safety of lasers used for display purposes* HSG95 HSE
    Books 1996 ISBN 978 0 7176 0691 7

4   *Code for lighting* CD-ROM CIBSE (Chartered Institute of Building
    Services Engineers) 2004 ISBN 978 1 903287 22 4

5   *The industrial environment* LG01 CIBSE 1999
    ISBN 978 0 900953 38 5 (O/P)

6   *Lighting Guide 7: Office lighting* LG07 CIBSE 2005
    ISBN 978 1 903287 52 1

7   BS 5489-1:2003 *Code of practice for the design of road lighting. Lighting
    of roads and public amenity areas* British Standards Institution 2003
    ISBN 978 0 580 42711 4

8   *Electrical safety on construction sites* HSG141 HSE Books 1995
    ISBN 978 0 7176 1000 6 (out of print)

9   *Lamp guide 2001* Lighting Industry Federation 2001 (free to
    download from www.lif.co.uk)

10 *Lighting in hostile and hazardous environments* CIBSE 1983
    ISBN 978 0 900953 26 2

11 BS 4800:1989 *Schedule of paint colours for building purposes* British
    Standards Institution 1989 ISBN 978 0 580 17196 3

12 *Emergency lighting* Technical Memorandum TM12 CIBSE 1986

13 BS 5266-1:1999 *Emergency lighting. Code of practice for the emergency
    lighting of premises other than cinemas and certain other specified
    premises used for entertainment* British Standards Institution 1999
    ISBN 978 0 580 33044 5

14 *The law on VDUs: An easy guide: Making sure your office complies with
    the Health and Safety (Display Screen Equipment) Regulations 1992 (as
    amended in 2002)* HSG90 (Second edition) HSE Books 2003
    ISBN 978 0 7176 2602 1

Further reading

Health and Safety Executive

Work with display screen equipment. Health and Safety (Display Screen Equipment) Regulations 1992 as amended by the Health and Safety (Miscellaneous Amendments) Regulations 2002. Guidance on Regulations L26 (Second edition) HSE Books 2003 ISBN 978 0 7176 2582 6

Safe use of work equipment. Provision and Use of Work Equipment Regulations 1998. Approved Code of Practice and guidance L22 (Third edition) HSE Books 2008 ISBN 978 0 7176 6295 1

Memorandum of guidance on the Electricity at Work Regulations 1989. Guidance on Regulations HSR25 (Second edition) HSE Books 2007 ISBN 978 0 7176 6228 9

Electrical safety on construction sites HSG141 HSE Books 1995 ISBN 978 0 7176 1000 6 (out of print)

COSHH a brief guide to the Regulations: What you need to know about the Control of Substances Hazardous to Health Regulations 2002 (COSHH) Leaflet INDG136(rev3) HSE Books 2005 www.hse.gov.uk/pubns/indg136.pdf

Control of substances hazardous to health (Fifth edition). The Control of Substances Hazardous to Health Regulations 2002 (as amended). Approved Code of Practice and guidance L5 (Fifth edition) HSE Books 2005 ISBN 978 0 7176 2981 7

British Standards Institution

BS 667:2005 *Illuminance meters. Requirements and test methods* British Standards Institution 2005 ISBN 978 0 580 44391 6

BS 1710:1984 *Specification for identification of pipelines and services* British Standards Institution 1984 ISBN 978 0 580 13859 1

BS 4533-102.1:1990 *Luminaires. Particular requirements. Specification for fixed general purpose luminaires* British Standards Institution 1990 ISBN 978 0 580 18900 5

BS 4800:1989 *Schedule of paint colours for building purposes* British Standards Institution 1989 ISBN 978 0 580 17196 3

BS 5266-1:1999 *Emergency lighting. Code of practice for the emergency lighting of premises other than cinemas and certain other specified premises used for entertainment* British Standards Institution 1999 ISBN 978 0 580 33044 5

BS IEC 60079-19:1993 *Electrical apparatus for explosive gas atmospheres. Repair and overhaul for apparatus used in explosive atmospheres (other than mines or explosives)* British Standards Institution 1997 ISBN 978 0 580 28548 6

BS ISO 8995:2002 *Lighting of indoor work places* British Standards Institution 2002 ISBN 978 0 580 39937 4

BS 8206-2:1992 *Lighting for buildings. Code of Practice for daylighting* British Standards Institution 1992 ISBN 978 0 580 20540 8

Chartered Institution of Building Services Engineers

Lighting Guide 2: Hospitals and health care buildings LG02 CIBSE 1989 ISBN 978 0 900953 37 8

Lighting Guide 3: Areas for visual display terminals LG03 CIBSE 1996 ISBN 978 0 900953 71 2

Lighting Guide 4: Sports LG04 CIBSE 1990 ISBN 978 0 900953 45 3

Lighting Guide: The visual environment in lecture, teaching and conference rooms LG05 CIBSE 1991 ISBN 978 0 900953 47 7

Lighting Guide: The outdoor environment LG06 CIBSE 1992 ISBN 978 0 900953 53 8

Lighting Guide: Lighting for museums and art galleries LG08 (Second edition) CIBSE 1994 ISBN 978 0 900953 65 1

The calculation and use of utilisation factors Technical Memorandum TM5 CIBSE 1980 (Black and white photocopies available only)

Lighting Industry Federation (LIF)

Hazardous area lighting LIF Fact finder 6 (O/P revised version to be available late 2002 on LIF website: www.lif.co.uk)

LIF Technical statements:

Capacitors containing polychlorinated biphenyls (PCBs) for fluorescent and discharge lighting Technical Statement 1 (free)

Fluorescent lighting and short switch-off periods Technical Statement 2 (free)

Energy limiters and tubular fluorescent lamps Technical Statement 3 (free)

Inductive luminaires and mineral insulated cables Technical Statement 5 (free)

Precautions against ultraviolet radiation from tungsten halogen lamps Technical Statement 6 (free)

Precautions against ultraviolet radiation from H.I.D lamps Technical Statement 7 (free)

UV radiation and health Technical Statement 8 (free)

Precautions against infra-red radiation from halogen heat lamps Technical Statement 9

National Radiological Protection Board

Health effects from ultraviolet radiation: Report of and Advisory Group of Non-ionising Radiation Vol 13 No 1 Documents of the NRPB 2002
ISBN 978 0 85951 475 0

S G Allen et al *Review of occupational exposure to optical radiation and electric and magnetic fields with regard to the proposed CEC Physical Agents Directive* NRPB-R265 1994 ISBN 978 0 85951 368 5

Other publications

Essentials of farm lighting (Ref: 4764) Electricity Council, Farm Electric 25

Threshold limit values for chemical substances and physical agents and biological exposure indices American Conference of Governmental Industrial Hygienists 1995-1996 ISBN 978 1 882417 11 7

IEC 825-1:1993 Published in UK as BS EN 60825-1:1994 *Safety of laser products. Equipment classification, requirements and user's guide* British Standards Institution 1994 ISBN 978 0 580 23532 0

IRPA guidelines on protection against non-ionising radiation Pergamon Press 1990 ISBN 978 0 08 036097 3

Photobiological safety for lamps and lamp systems. General requirements ANSI/IESNA RP-27.1.96 ISBN 978 0 87995 139 9

Photobiological safety for lamps and lamp systems. Risk group classification and labelling ANSI/IESNA RP-27.3.96 ISBN 978 0 87995 140 5

Boyce P R *Human factors in lighting* Applied Science Publishers 1980
ISBN 978 0 853349 12 9

Hopkinson R G and Collins J B *The ergonomics of lighting* Macdonald Technical and Scientific 1970 ISBN 978 0 35 602680 0

Cayliss M A and Marsden A M *Lamps and lighting* Edward Arnold 1983
ISBN 978 0 71 313487 2

De Boer J B and Fischer D *Interior lighting* Philips Technical Library

Lumsden W K et al *Outdoor lighting handbook* Gower Press 1974 ISBN 978 0 71 610297 7

Lyons S L *Exterior lighting for industry and security* Applied Science Publishers 1980 ISBN 978 0 85 334879 5

Lyons S L *Lighting for industry and security: A handbook for providers and users of lighting* Butterworth Heinemann 1993 ISBN 978 0 75 061084 1

While every effort has been made to ensure the accuracy of the references listed in this publication, their future availability cannot be guaranteed.

Useful addresses

British Standards Institution, Customer Services, 389 Chiswick High Road, London W4 4AL Tel: 020 8996 9001

Chartered Institution of Building Services Engineers, Delta House, 222 Balham High Road, London SW12 9BS Tel: 020 8675 5211

Lighting Industry Federation Ltd, Ground Floor, Westminster Tower, 3 Albert Embankment, London SE1 7SL Tel: 020 7793 3020

Health Protection Agency, Centre for Radiation, Chemical and Environmental Hazards, Chilton, Didcot, Oxon OX11 0RQ Tel: 01235 833891

Glossary

Control systems	Systems that control the switching and/or dimming of a lighting installation.
Directional lighting	Lighting designed to illuminate a task or surface predominantly from one direction.
Disability glare	Glare produced directly or by reflection that impairs the visibility of objects without necessarily causing discomfort.
Discomfort glare	Glare that causes visual discomfort.
Emergency lighting	Lighting provided for use when the main lighting installation fails.
General lighting	Lighting designed to illuminate the whole of an area uniformly, without provision for special lighting requirements.
Glare	The discomfort or impairment of vision experienced when parts of the visual field are excessively bright in relation to the general surroundings.
Illuminance (lux)	The luminous flux density at a surface, ie the luminous flux incident per unit area. It is measured in lux = lumens/square metre.
Illumination	The process of lighting.

Indirect lighting	Lighting where most of the light reaches a surface, usually on a working plane, only after reflection off other surfaces.
Infra-red radiation	Electromagnetic radiation in the wavelength range 760 nano-metres - 1 millimetre.
Local lighting	Lighting designed to illuminate a particular small area which usually does not extend far beyond the task.
Localised lighting	Lighting designed to illuminate an interior and at the same time provide higher illuminances over particular areas or parts of an interior.
Luminaire	Light fitting which includes the components necessary for fixing and supporting the lamp, and for connecting it to the supply circuit. It also controls the distribution of light produced by a lamp or lamps.
Luminous efficiency	The ratio of luminous flux to the lamp power. Measured in units of lumens/watts.
Luminous flux (lumen)	The rate of flow of luminous energy at a given point from a light source. One lumen = 1 candela steradian (cd.sr).
Mounting height	The vertical distance between a luminaire and the working plane.
Reflectance	The ratio between the luminous flux reflected from a surface and the luminous flux falling on it.

Spacing/mounting height	The ratio between the distance from the luminaire centre to the height of the luminaire above a horizontal working plane.
Ultra-violet radiation	Electromagnetic radiation in the wavelength range 100 nano-metres - 400 nano-metres.
Veiling reflections	Reflections from a light source that mask the visibility of a task.
Visual field	The full extent of what can be seen by the visual system when looking in a given direction.
Visual system	The combination of eye, optic nerve and brain which provides sense of seeing.
Working plane	The horizontal, vertical or inclined plane on which the task lies.

Printed and published by the Health and Safety Executive   08/09   C10